The Usborne TRAVEL Activity Book

Written by

Rebecca Gilpin, Lucy Bowman
and Will Severs

Designed and illustrated by

Erica Harrison, Laurent Kling,
Sophie Crichton, Benedetta Giaufret, Enrica Rusinà,
Fred Blunt, Non Figg and Alex Mathers

Edited by Fiona Watt

You'll find the answers and solutions
to the puzzles on pages 92-96.

GETTING READY

EARLY START

Lisa is catching an early flight to Japan this morning. She needs to set her alarm clock, but isn't sure what time for. Can you figure it out?

She needs to be at the airport two hours before departure, to check in.

It will take her 15 minutes to eat breakfast.

She needs 5 minutes to brush her teeth.

The car journey to the airport takes 45 minutes.

10:30

Her flight departs at 10.30 a.m.

It will take her half an hour to have a shower and get dressed.

Lisa needs to set her alarm clock for ....

MIX-UP

Rob and Michael are going on different trips. Rob is going on a wildlife safari in Kenya and Michael is going skiing in the Alps. Can you figure out which items each will need to pack? Draw a line between the items and who they belong to, using a different pen for each. Some items don't need to be packed.

Rob

Michael

WHERE TO GO?

Jamal is trying to decide where he would most like to visit.
Where do you think he should go?

☆ He wants to swim every day
☆ He doesn't like the cold
☆ He likes animals
☆ He doesn't like eating fish
☆ He wants to explore some ancient buildings

GREENLAND

• Go dog sledding across the snow.

• Relax in our indoor spa and heated pool.

BARBADOS

• Snorkel among the coral reefs and swim with leatherback turtles.

• Feast on a local speciality of grilled tuna.

Egypt

• Visit the pyramids, built over 4000 years ago.

• Enjoy a swim in our outdoor swimming pool.

• Ride a camel across the hot desert sands.

Australia

• See wild kangaroos or koalas in their natural habitat.

• Swim and surf in the sea.

• Visit the amazing Sydney Opera House.

PACKING

Look closely at Josie's list of things to pack for her trip for one minute. Then, cover the list with your hand, and draw around every item you can remember.

Sun hat
Camera
Beach towel
Sunscreen
Sandals
Magazine
Blue dress
Music player

Is there anything that Josie needs to pack that isn't here?   YES / NO

BUSY AIRPORT

Lots of people are at this airport, ready to fly off to places all around the world. Can you spot the following?:

☆ Two people reading books
☆ Someone putting on their shoes
☆ Two men who have fallen asleep
☆ Five people pulling suitcases on wheels
☆ A child playing with a toy car
☆ Someone eating a sandwich
☆ A boy riding on a luggage trolley
☆ Someone buying a magazine
☆ A lady in an orange top

à la mode

NEWSAGENT

SNACK SHOP

Air Usborne   Air Usborne   Air Usborne   Air Usborne

5

GOING PLACES

CITY WALK

Jim and Joe are enjoying a leisurely walk back to their hotel. Which way do they go?

Begin at the START, then follow the instructions at each intersection:
R = turn right, L = turn left, S = go straight on.

R R L S R L R S R R L S S R S L L S S L

☆ Do they walk past the church?

☆ Can you spot a sign with an ice cream on it?

START

Hotel

Museum

HOTEL

HOTEL

CROSSING RIVERS

The people in the pictures below are trying to cross rivers. Help them by drawing a line from each river to the best way of crossing it. One line has been drawn, to start you off.

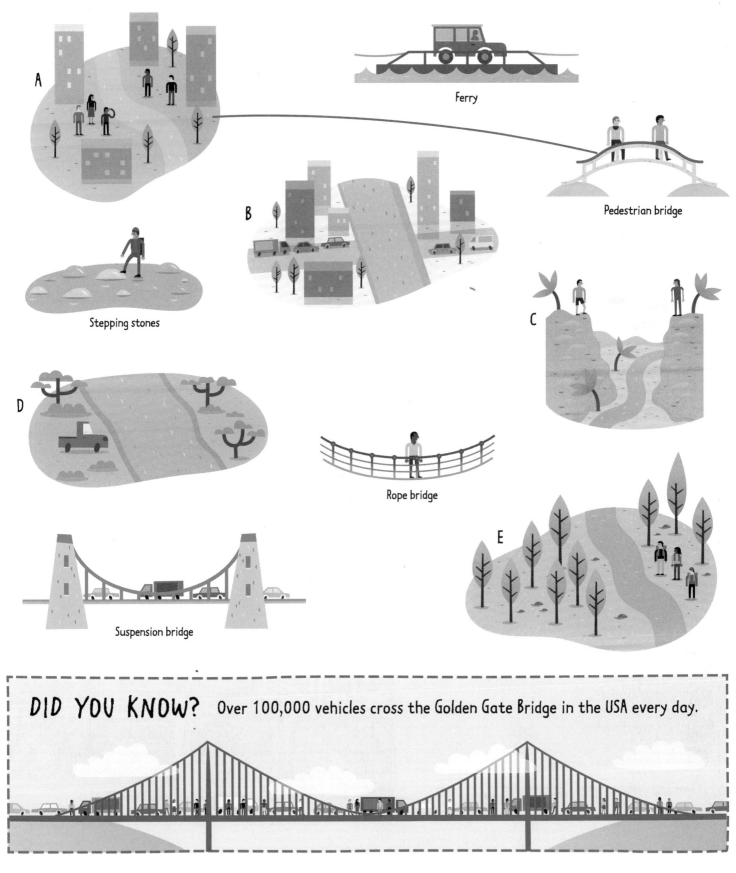

A

Ferry

Pedestrian bridge

B

Stepping stones

C

D

Rope bridge

E

Suspension bridge

DID YOU KNOW? Over 100,000 vehicles cross the Golden Gate Bridge in the USA every day.

A WORLD OF FOOD

DIFFERENT TASTES

In which country are you most likely to eat these foods?
Draw a line to link each kind of food with the correct country.

chicken feet

Italy

fish eggs (caviar)

Canada

kangaroo steak

goat stew

maple syrup

Australia

Ghana

snails in garlic butter

China

France

England

folded pizza (calzone)

Russia

jellied eels

FRUIT AND VEGETABLES

Mateo has a list of fruit and vegetables to buy. Find each item and write on the list the square or squares it is in. The first one has been done for you.

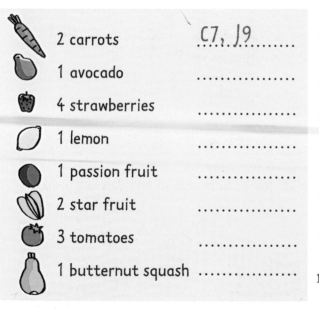

2 carrots	C7, J9
1 avocado	....
4 strawberries	....
1 lemon	....
1 passion fruit	....
2 star fruit	....
3 tomatoes	....
1 butternut squash	....

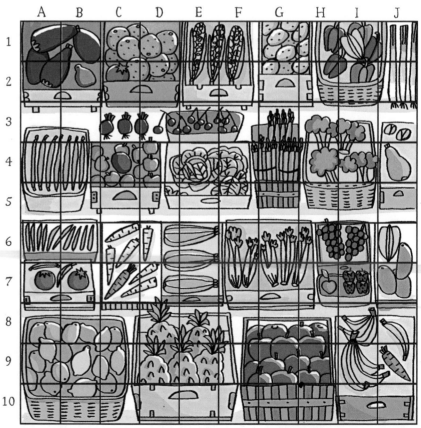

Does Mateo find everything he needs? Draw a line under the correct answer: YES / NO

FOOD FINDER

Can you find these foods from around the world on the plate? They go across, up, down and some may go backward. Cross them off as you find them.

BRATWURST (German sausage)

COLCANNON (Irish mashed potato and cabbage dish)

FALAFEL (Middle Eastern fried balls made from chickpeas)

GAZPACHO (cold soup from Spain)

GUACAMOLE (mashed avocado dip or spread from Mexico)

JAMBALAYA (meat, seafood, vegetable and rice dish from the southern states of America)

NAAN (a flatbread from India)

PESTO (Italian basil-based pasta sauce)

RATATOUILLE (French vegetable stew)

SOUVLAKI (Greek skewer of cooked small pieces of meat)

```
    N A H S P
  G A Z P A C H O I   I
F A L E F A L A F   C T
O Y I C O L F K U O S
A R A T A T O U I L L E A
M I L W H G J L A Y C T N
B R A T W U R S T Y A M A
J A B R P E S T O B N N A N
A T M O L N A D V A A P A
  F A L I K A L V U O S
  O J A M L W X A G N F
  G U A C A M O L E
      P E S V T
```

TASTY KEBABS

The pieces of food on each of these kebabs follow a sequence, but there are some gaps. See if you can figure out each sequence, then draw the missing pieces.

SHARING SUSHI

Keiko and her friends are eating sushi. Is there enough for all of them to have one of each type?

9

WHEN IN ROME

IN THE FORUM

These tourists are too busy looking at the ruins to notice eight Ancient Romans hidden amongst them. Can you spot them?

MOPED MAZE

Which way should this moped go through the streets of Rome to Vatican City, crossing the River Tiber on the way?

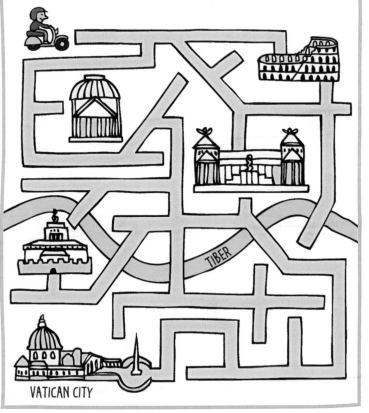

ITALIAN PHRASEBOOK

Ciao (chow)	Hello *or* goodbye
Buona sera (bwoh-nah-seh-rah)	Good evening
Buona notte (bwoh-nah noht-teh)	Goodnight
Come stai? (koh-meh sty)	How are you?
Sto bene (stoh beh-neh)	I'm fine
Come ti chiami? (koh-meh tee kee-ah-mee)	What's your name?
Mi chiamo... (mee kee-ah mo)	My name is...
Per favore (pehr-fah-voh-reh)	Please
Grazie (graht-zee-eh)	Thanks

uno (oo-noh)	1	*sei (say)*	6
due (doo-eh)	2	*sette (seht-teh)*	7
tre (treh)	3	*otto (aw-toh)*	8
quattro (kwaht-troh)	4	*nove (naw-vay)*	9
cinque (cheen-kweh)	5	*dieci (dee-ay-chee)*	10

GELATO JOY

A trip to Rome isn't complete without some delicious ice cream, or *gelato*. Can you unscramble the letters below to find out which ice cream each child is asking for?

BARRYWERTS

THOLOCACE

IATSOCHIP

NAVALLI

Milo

Sophia

Teresa

Milo wants... ....

Sophia wants... ....

Teresa wants... ....

....

ON THE GO

Use orange and blue pens to complete this busy scene.

Finish the buildings.

Complete the train.

Draw more seashells and sandcastles.

Draw more sun rays.

Doodle more trees in the park.

Add more cars.

13

ON THE QUAYSIDE

At this port, cars and trucks are waiting for a ferry, people are boarding a passenger ferry, and boats are moored at the quayside. Fill the scene with stickers from the sticker pages: read each label, find the correct sticker, then press it over the label.

A motor boat

A truck with a picture of flowers on the side

A yellow car with a white stripe

A green truck

A lady on a yellow moped

CALVIN'S CARROTS

A blue car with a luggage rack

A seagull

A group of people on board the ferry

Three more lifeboats

A family group having their photo taken

A blue car pulling a trailer

Three hikers with backp[...]

A red sports car

A broken-down car

A couple with a lot of bags

A jeep

A white car

A VISIT TO RUSSIA

Russia is a huge country, filled with many contrasts and things to see.

DAZZLING DOMES

St Basil's Cathedral in Moscow has brightly patterned domes. Complete the picture by filling in each shape with a pen that matches the dot inside it.

TRANS-SIBERIAN RAILWAY

Tess is on a train from Moscow to Vladivostok and she's taking lots of photos as the train travels along.

Tess

Tess couldn't have taken one of these photos. Which one is it?

A B C D

RUSSIAN DOLLS

Which doll in this set is the odd one out? (Ignore the difference in size.)

A B C D E F

QUICK QUIZ

Draw a line under each correct answer.

1. You might eat 'blinis' in Russia. Are they:
   Gherkins? Little pancakes?
   Tiny fish? Mini sausages?

2. In parts of Russia, it sometimes never gets dark.
   True / False

3. Which type of dance is Russia most famous for?
   Salsa / Ballet / Tap / Limbo / Tango

DID YOU KNOW?

Wild tigers live in some parts of Russia.

PALM TREES AND PYRAMIDS

PILES OF STONE

Each pyramid contains a word related to Egypt, but there are two extra letters in each one. Unscramble the letters to find the words. Write each word below its pyramid.

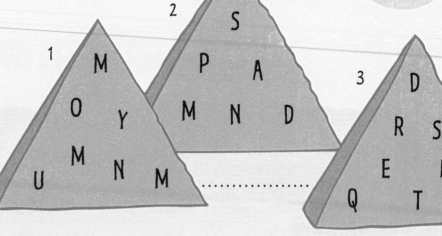

1. M O Y M U N M N

2. S P A M N D

3. D R S E Q I E T E

THIRSTY CAMELS

These camels need a drink of water. Which camels find the oasis and which get lost?

These camels find the oasis: ....

These camels get lost: ....

18

MUSEUM TREASURES

Each of these Ancient Egyptian treasures has a pair, apart from one. Draw a line linking each object to its twin, then draw around the one that is different.

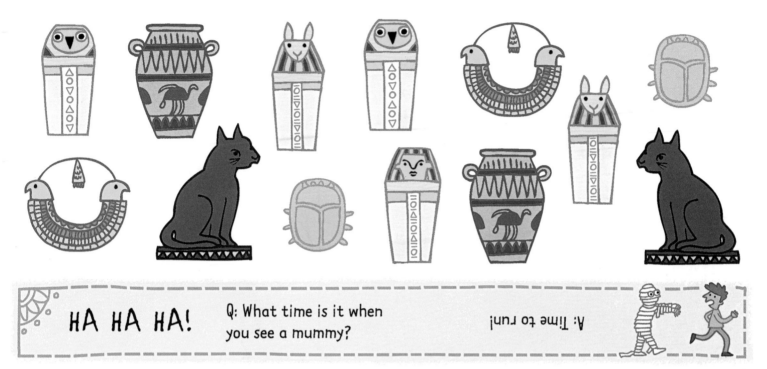

HA HA HA!

Q: What time is it when you see a mummy?

A: Time to run!

SECRETS OF THE SPHINX

There are many mysteries about the Sphinx, including how and why it was made. See if you can uncover some of its secrets by answering these questions. Draw a line under each correct answer.

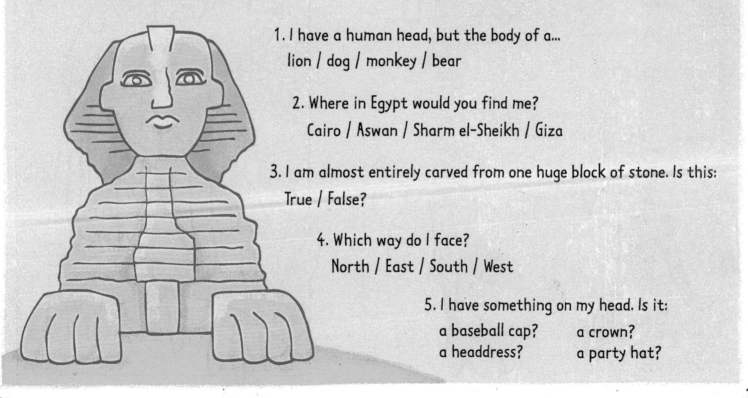

1. I have a human head, but the body of a...
lion / dog / monkey / bear

2. Where in Egypt would you find me?
Cairo / Aswan / Sharm el-Sheikh / Giza

3. I am almost entirely carved from one huge block of stone. Is this:
True / False?

4. Which way do I face?
North / East / South / West

5. I have something on my head. Is it:
a baseball cap?   a crown?
a headdress?   a party hat?

STUNNING SOUTH AMERICA

LUSH RAINFOREST

The Amazon rainforest is teeming with wildlife, but which creature would you not expect to see there?

Leaf cutter ant

Toucan

Butterfly

Sloth

Tapir

Turtle

Boa constrictor

Tree frog

Puffin

LOST SPOTS

Lots of this jaguar's markings are missing. Doodle markings on the rest of his body.

BRIGHT BIRDS

Complete this picture of macaws by filling in each shape with a pen that matches the dot inside it.

HERDING ON HORSEBACK

This Argentinian gaucho is herding cattle. Are there more dark brown, light brown or white cows?

There are more .... cows.

ANCIENT STONES

There are ancient walls in Peru in which the stones are fitted tightly together. Which of these stones should be in the gap?

1   2   3   ④

FUN FABRICS

In the Andes, there is a tradition of weaving bright fabrics. Can you spot these three fabrics in the pile below?

A   B   C

21

EXCITING SPORTS

HANG-GLIDING

Can you put these pictures in the correct order?
Start with setting up the hang-glider.

A

B

C

D

ON THE PISTE

Without taking your pen off the paper, take this snowboarder from the top to the bottom of the slope. Avoid obstacles, other snowboarders and skiers, and see if you can leap over some jumps, too.

DID YOU KNOW?

Kitesurfing is an extreme sport in which people surf on a board attached to a huge kite. Sometimes they take off and twist and turn in the air!

RIDING THE RAPIDS

Which route does this kayaker take down the river?
Looking at the clues below, see if you can figure it out.

☆ The kayaker goes between two small rocks
☆ He goes very close to the bank twice
☆ He passes a bird on a rock

He takes route ....

A B C D

Can you spot and draw
around the following?:

☆ Four deer
☆ A wolf
☆ Four birds
☆ A bear
☆ Five rabbits

23

TRAVEL GAMES

PACKING A SUITCASE

Play this memory game with as many people as you like.

1. The first person thinks of something they've packed in an imaginary suitcase, beginning with the letter A.

> In my suitcase I packed an atlas...

2. The next person repeats what the first person said, then adds something new, beginning with the letter B.

> In my suitcase I packed an atlas and boots...

3. The game continues through the alphabet. If someone gets something wrong, or forgets something, they are out.

> In my suitcase I packed an atlas, boots, cards, a dog, an envelope, a fountain pen and... er...?

4. The last person still playing is the winner.

BRAVE EXPLORERS

Play this somewhere you can lie down safely.

1. Choose someone to be a sleeping crocodile. Everyone else is an explorer. The crocodile lies on the floor and closes his eyes.

Crocodile

2. The explorers have to creep up to the sleeping crocodile and try to touch him. The crocodile can open his eyes at any time. If the crocodile sees someone moving, he 'eats' them.

Anyone who stays still is safe.

3. If an explorer manages to touch the crocodile, that explorer wins. If the crocodile spots all the explorers, he wins.

SPOTTING GAME

This is a game for two people to play on a trip, or just when they're out and about.

1. Ask someone else to be the 'caller'. Then, close your eyes.

2. The caller shouts out something to spot. Both of you open your eyes.

3. The first person to spot that thing wins.

A van!

There's one!

WHAT COUNTRY?

1. One person thinks of a country.

Mexico

2. The other person shuts their eyes and holds out a hand, with the palm facing up.

3. The first person uses a fingertip to slowly spell out the country on their friend's hand. Their friend has to guess what it is, one letter at a time.

M...E...X... Mexico?

4. When they've managed to guess it, it's their turn to think of a country.

TRAVEL SHAPES

To play this, you will need some paper and some pens.

1. Each person chooses a different shape, such as a circle, square, rectangle or triangle.

Triangle!   Circle!   Square!

2. Someone thinks of a travel-related subject to draw. It could be anything at all: the seaside, a campsite, a city or a countryside scene.

Seaside

3. Everyone draws the subject, using only the shape that they've chosen. This may be quite hard to do! Everyone shows their pictures to each other.

IN THE CITY

Like many places around the world, this city has lots of tall buildings and skyscrapers. Can you complete all the puzzles and activities?

Complete this building. --→

Reading across the windows from the top of the building to the bottom, can you find the names of four places around the world with lots of skyscrapers?

(Clue: look at the capital letters.)

a	H	m	v	O
i	p	N	k	y
G	u	K	h	o
w	O	b	N	e
n	j	G	N	q
E	o	W	f	u
a	Y	c	n	O
R	d	K	x	e
D	d	q	U	h
f	B	o	c	A
p	g	I	f	e
m	T	u	x	O
K	o	i	Y	c
b	h	O	n	p
g	v	m	a	j

How many birds are there on this building's window ledges? Fill them in as you count them.

Total ..18.....

Starting here, can you find a route up to the top of this skyscraper?

—— —— ——

—— —— ——

—— ——

—— ——

Each of these sudoku puzzles contains four different pictures. Each puzzle must have one of each picture in each row, column and 4-square box.

Add windows to this skyscraper.

A   B   C   D

Can you spot these windows in the building above?

TRAIN TRIP

Jack and Sadie are meeting to catch a train. Follow the instructions below to help Jack find Sadie, drawing his route as you go.

Walk past the ticket machines... go to the left of the lady with the striped suitcase... up between the two trees... behind the boy taking a photo... then in front of a man reading a newspaper... past two friends hugging... in front of a girl who's waving... down to the striped umbrellas... past the flower stall... to the lady with the baby... around the left side of the souvenir stall... past the flower box and the man with the red suitcase...
There's Sadie!

Fleur's flowers

FANTASTIC FESTIVALS

CARNIVAL COSTUMES

It's Mardi Gras in New Orleans, USA. Armand is trying to find his sister Leonie, but she's dressed up for the carnival. Can you identify her from these clues?

☆ She has wings
☆ She doesn't have claws
☆ She doesn't have spots
☆ She isn't wearing white

.... is Leonie

MONKEYING AROUND

Each year, a huge banquet is held for the monkeys that live in Lopburi in Thailand. Fill the table with food and monkey stickers from the sticker pages.

LIGHTS AND PATTERNS

At the Hindu festival of Diwali, people light oil lamps and make 'Rangoli' decorations on the floor with rice powder, flour or petals. Use pens or pencils to fill in these Rangoli patterns.

Diwali lamp ----

DID YOU KNOW?

In the town of Buñol in Spain, there's a messy festival called La Tomatina, in which thousands of people throw squashy tomatoes at each other.

TRAVEL DOODLES

DESIGN A T-SHIRT

Design a souvenir T-shirt from somewhere you've been or somewhere you'd like to go.

SEAGULLS

Doodle eyes, beaks, wings and feathers.

TRAVEL DIARY

Complete this diary by drawing pictures of the activities being described.
You could also add more activities and draw pictures of them.

I went to the beach and set up a blue and white striped beach umbrella.

I bought an ice cream cone filled with a scoop of strawberry and a scoop of chocolate.

I swam in the sea, but got out quickly when I saw a jellyfish.

I made a sandcastle in the sand, and decorated it with orange seashells.

POSTAGE STAMPS

Grab some pens or pencils and create your own stamps. You could draw pictures of places around the world or ways of getting around. Add the price of the stamp, too.

HISTORIC CITY

Complete these old buildings with a black pen. Add windows, doors, bricks and roof tiles, then fill in the picture.

AT THE SEASIDE

A DAY ON THE BEACH

Each person on the beach needs a towel, an umbrella, a bag, a ball and sunglasses – are there enough items for them all? Draw a line under the correct answer:

YES / NO

IN... AND OUT...

The changing tide has moved things in this rock pool. Can you spot nine differences? Draw around each one.

CHOPPY SEA

Each line of waves follows a sequence, but there are some gaps. Figure out which shape of wave is missing from each line, then draw it in.

HA HA HA!

Q: Where can you find an ocean without water?

A: On a globe!

34

ON THE SEA FRONT

Alice and Cally are sitting in the sun. There are so many people around, they haven't spotted that two of their friends are nearby. Can you spot them?

☆ Asha is wearing sunglasses... doesn't have red hair... is eating an ice cream... and is scared of dogs.

☆ Ruby is talking on a phone... is wearing a hat... likes stripes... and is carrying a bag.

Alice   Cally

SEAL SANCTUARY

It's the seals' feeding time, but which one is most hungry? To find out, cross off the numbers on the seals as you answer the clues below. The one that's left is hungriest. Draw a fish in its mouth.

What is the number of...
☆ Wings on five seagulls?
☆ Eyes of nine fish?
☆ Arms and legs of three fishermen?
☆ Seals in this picture?
☆ Points on three starfish?
☆ Times the sun rises in a week?
☆ Flippers on three scuba divers?
☆ Legs on an octopus?

BIG WORLD QUIZ

1. Which of these would you be surprised to see in Tanzania?

a) a wombat
b) a flamingo
c) a wildebeest

2. One of these is on the Brazilian flag – which one?

a) a parrot in a circle
b) a globe with a starry sky
c) a dragon

3. In which of these rivers might you find piranha fish?

a) Amazon, South America
b) Seine, France
c) Yangtze, China

4. If you buy a 'naranja' in Spain, what have you bought?

a) a banana
b) an orange
c) an apple

5. Which of these historic landmarks is oldest?

a) The Alhambra, Spain
b) The Colosseum, Italy
c) Stonehenge, England

6. In which US state would you find the Grand Canyon?

a) Montana
b) Colorado
c) Arizona

7. On which continent are the Himalayas?

a) South America
b) Europe
c) Asia

8. What is the famous mountain near Cape Town, South Africa?

a) Chair Mountain
b) Table Mountain
c) Bed Mountain

9. One of these is not a sea. Which one?

a) Blue Sea
b) Black Sea
c) Red Sea

10. Lake Baikal is the world's deepest lake. Where is it?

a) Russia
b) Nepal
c) Peru

11. Which of these is Australia's capital city?

a) Sydney
b) Canberra
c) Melbourne

12. In Hong Kong, you might see a traditional sailing ship, called a:

a) junk
b) bunk
c) sunk

13. Which of these countries shares a border with Argentina?

a) Mexico
b) Venezuela
c) Chile

14. In France, a sign to 'la plage' is pointing to:

a) the town square
b) the beach
c) the shops

15. Which of these dishes does not include rice?

a) Italian risotto
b) Chinese chow mein
c) Spanish paella

16. The temple of Angkor Wat is in which of these countries?

a) Cambodia
b) Egypt
c) Greece

17. If you're on the Brooklyn Bridge, where are you?

a) London, England
b) New York, USA
c) Ottawa, Canada

18. Where would you find the cave paintings at Lascaux?

a) Mexico
b) Bulgaria
c) France

19. If you order spaghetti carbonara in Italy, which of these will the sauce contain?

a) beef and tomato
b) cream, garlic and vegetable
c) egg, cheese and bacon

20. If you went to every country in the world, roughly how many would you have visited?

a) 100
b) 200
c) 300

21. If you say 'auf Wiedersehen' in German, which of these are you saying?:

a) It's so hot
b) It's just over there
c) Goodbye

22. Why might you be unable to sleep in the Arctic in the summer?

a) it's light all night
b) the polar bears are noisy
c) there's lots of traffic

23. Which of these might you see if you go to Sicily, Italy?

a) Mount Fuji
b) Mount Kilimanjaro
c) Mount Etna

24. If you go to a souk in Morocco, are you going:

a) swimming?
b) shopping?
c) camel riding?

25. Which of these animals are you least likely to see in Mongolia?

a) camels
b) horses
c) llamas

26. If you're in Machu Picchu, which of these is most useful?

a) skis
b) walking boots
c) swimwear

27. Where are you unlikely to see an international cricket match?

a) Portugal
b) India
c) Australia

28. One of these isn't a real canal. Which one?

a) Corsica Canal
b) Suez Canal
c) Panama Canal

29. Which of these big cats is from Africa?

a) cheetah
b) jaguar
c) snow leopard

30. What's most likely to be on the menu in Sweden?

a) barbecued sausages
b) slow-roasted duck
c) pickled herring

31. Where are you most likely to enjoy surfing?

a) Hawaii
b) Bolivia
c) Greece

32. You're visiting a rainforest. Are you in:

a) Greenland?
b) Ireland?
c) Indonesia?

33. Which ocean is between North America and Europe?

a) Atlantic
b) Pacific
c) Indian

34. You might hear someone from New Zealand being called:

a) an Emu
b) an Ostrich
c) a Kiwi

35. Which country uses money that is not a kind of dollar?

a) United States of America
b) New Zealand
c) Egypt

36. Which of these places does not have a beach?

a) Bondi, Australia
b) Pisa, Italy
c) Copacabana, Brazil

When you've done the quiz, fill in the pictures.

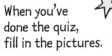

AWESOME AUSTRALIA

GOING WALKABOUT

Rachel's hiking in the bush. Which path leads to the stream, and which one brings her back to her starting point?

..D... = stream ...B.. = starting point

SIGHTSEEING CONUNDRUM

The places in Dom's guidebook have been given 1, 2 or 3 smiles by people who have visited them. He's going to visit the place with the most smiles. Add them up to see where he'll go. The first one's been started for you.

A. Sydney Opera House

2 people $1 \times 2 = 2$ $2 + 8 +$
4 people $2 \times 4 = 8$
3 people ....   Total smiles: ......

B. Uluru (Ayers Rock)

1 person ....
2 people ....
5 people ....   Total smiles: ......

C. The Great Barrier Reef

3 people ....
3 people ....
4 people ....   Total smiles: ......

Dom will visit .....

SLEEPY KOALA

Kiki the koala can only reach her sleeping place by climbing past answers that are odd numbers. Which way does she need to go?

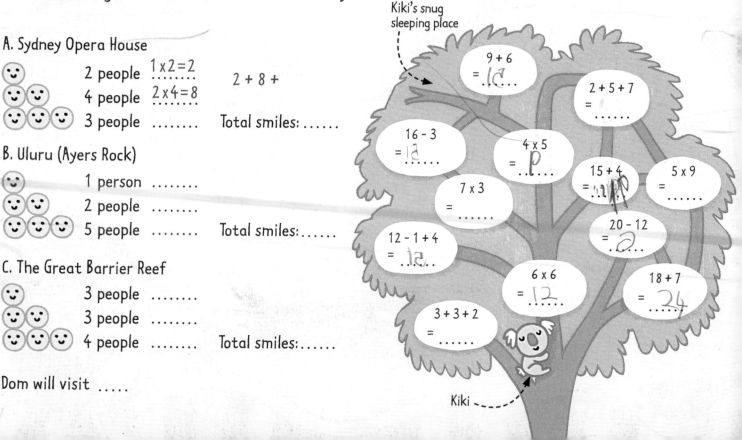

Kiki's snug sleeping place

$9 + 6$ = 15

$2 + 5 + 7$ = 1.

$16 - 3$ = 12

4×5 = P

$15 + 4$ = 19

5×9 =

7×3 =

$20 - 12$ = 2

$12 - 1 + 4$ = 12

6×6 = 12

$18 + 7$ = 24

$3 + 3 + 2$ =

Kiki ----

LOTS OF SPOTS

complete this Aboriginal-style picture by filling in the shapes.
Use a pen that matches the dot inside each shape.

HIKING AND BIKING

HAPPY HIKER

Help the hiker find his way through the forest back to his log cabin.

Triplets Brad, Chad and Tad are setting off on a hike. Spot and draw around one thing that's different about each of them.

There are three strange things about this hiker. Can you spot them?

BRAVE BIKERS

Three mountain bikers have just finished a race, but who won? Look at how many points each obstacle is worth, then add up the points along each route. The biker with the fewest points won the race.

Mud = 3

Fallen tree = 4

Jump = -1

START

A

B

C

Biker .... won, with .... points.

MOUNTAIN BIKES

Fill in these mountain bikes.

Can you spot an abandoned bike and a lost hiker somewhere on these two pages?

ON TOP OF THE WORLD

WHICH MOUNTAIN?

Can you match these famous mountains to their names? Draw a line between them.

1

2

3

4

Devils Tower, USA

Uluru (Ayers Rock), Australia

Mount Kilimanjaro, Tanzania

Mount Fuji, Japan

CLIMBING HIGH

The climber at the bottom will collect points whenever he passes a handhold in the rock. Can you find a route to the top that will give him a score of 20?

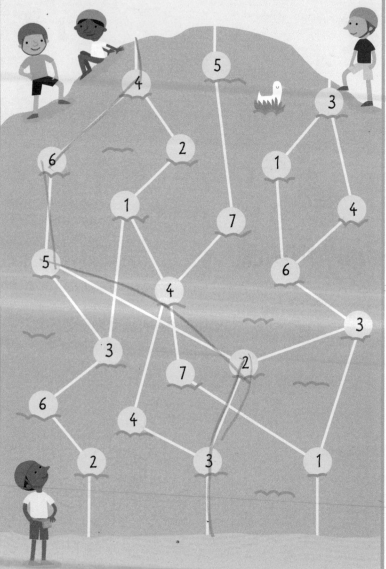

DID YOU KNOW?

There are huge mountains at the bottom of the sea. The tops of some make islands above the water.

MOUNTAIN CROSSING

This snow leopard needs to reach a cave on the other side of the mountains. Can you find a path, through the breaks in the mountains and the snow?

This is a break.

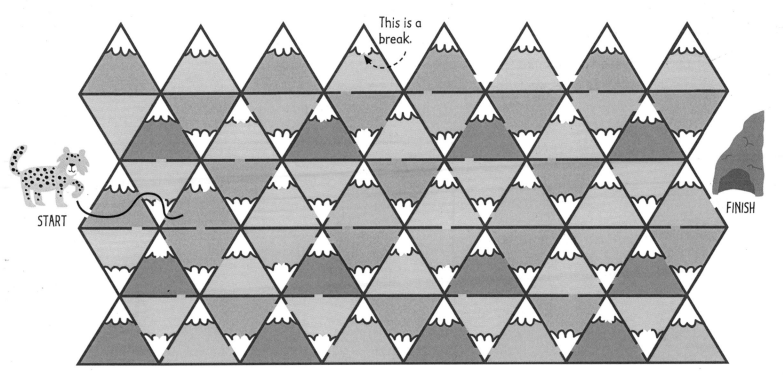

START

FINISH

WILD FLOWERS

In Spring and Summer, many mountainous places are covered with flowers. Count how many there are here, filling them in as you go.

How many flowers are there? ....

PRAYER FLAGS

Each of these lines of Himalayan prayer flags follows a sequence. Can you identify each sequence, then fill in the blank flags?

ON THE ROAD
WHO GOES WHERE?

One of these cars is on its way to the sea, one is going to the mountains, and one is going to the city. Follow the instructions below to find out where each car goes, and the route it takes to get there.

N = North   E = East
S = South   W = West

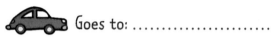 Goes to: ....

E E S S E S S S S E E E S S E S S E S

W S W W W N N N

 Goes to: ....

E E E S W S E E E E E E S E E E S S S

S S S S W W W W W N E E N E N N

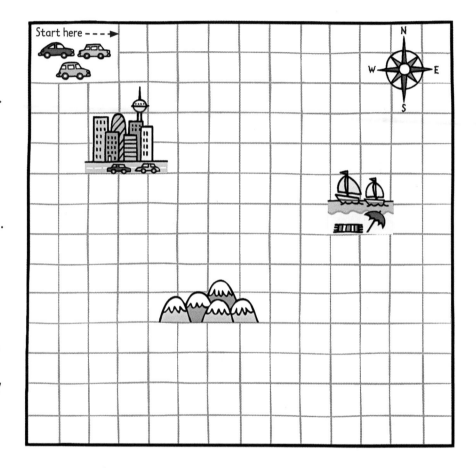

Goes to: ....

E E E E S S E S E S S W S S E S S S W

S W W W W W N N N N W N N N E

WHICH ORDER?

Looking at the clues, can you figure out which order the four cars are in? When you have, press on the car stickers from the sticker pages.

☆ Green isn't next to white.   ☆ Red is in front of green.   ☆ Blue is at the back.

THINGS TO SEE

Tilly and Tom are on a long car journey, and they're spotting things out of the window. They've each got a system to note down what they've seen. Who's seen more cows so far, and who's seen more houses?

I replace the first letter of each word with the next letter in the alphabet.

Tilly

uree   iouse
dow
eog
uree   iouse   uree
eog   dow
tign
theep   iouse
uree
dow   uree
iouse
dow
uree   uree

I write each word back to front, starting with its last letter.

Tom

eert
esuoh   woc
eert   hcruhc
woc   peehs
tac   esuoh
eert   eert   tac
woc
esuoh   woc
rotcart   eert
woc   peehs

.... has seen more cows.   .... has seen more houses.

DESERT ROAD TRIP

These cars have just passed each other on a long road through the desert. Each car should be symmetrical, but half of each one is missing. Can you complete them?

(If you imagine dividing each car down the middle with a straight line, each half should be an exact reflection of the other.)

Draw this man's twin in the other seat of the car.

Add more dust clouds, too.

HA HA HA!

Q: How do you stop a dog from howling in the back of a car?

A: Let it sit in the front.

Awoooo

45

SPACE TRAVEL

Some people have already been into space as tourists. In the future, it should become easier and easier to be a space tourist. For now, here's your chance...

READY TO GO?

Each of these space tourists needs a helmet, a spacesuit, boots and a camera. Have any of them forgotten anything? Write your answers below them.

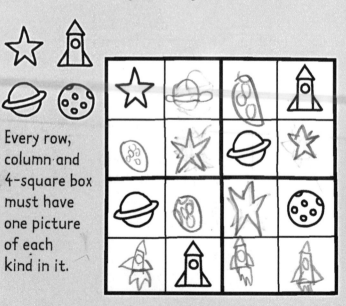

A

B

C .... camera

SPACE SUDOKU

Complete the grid below by drawing pictures of these four things you might see in space.

Every row, column and 4-square box must have one picture of each kind in it.

BLAST OFF!

This rocket is ready to launch. Make your way to its top by finding five words related to space. Each word links up with the next.

s t a r
p l a _ _ _
_ _ _ _ _ _
_ _ _ _
_ _ _

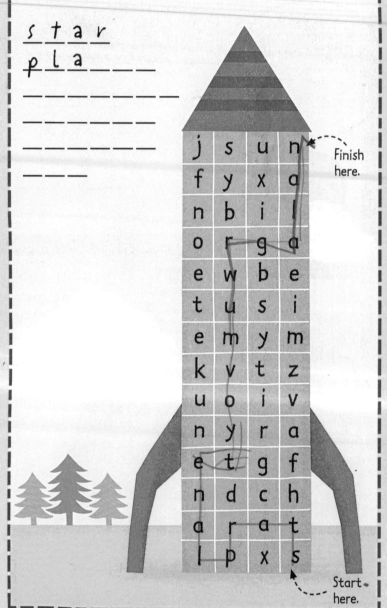

Finish here.

Start here.

HA HA HA!

Q: Did you hear about the astronaut who put on a clean pair of socks every day?

A: By the end of the week, he couldn't get his boots on!

SPACE DESTINATIONS

The codes below are hiding five space destinations.
To crack them, look at the planets on the right.
Each code number is a letter on one of the planets.
The first destination has been written in for you.

Write your answers here:

1. 5 7 7 4
2. 5 2 4 4
3. 6 3 2 5 3 7 4
4. 4 2 3 3 4 4
5. 3 4 2 4 3 4

1. M O O N
2. mars
3. _ _ _ _ _ _ _
4. _ _ _ _ _ _
5. _ _ _ _ _ _

1. b v w x

2. a y z p

3. c d u t

4. g r s n

5. m i k h

6. l f j

7. o e q

SPACE LOG

Imagine you're a tourist on a space trip. Record your journey in the logbook below, looking at the words and pictures for ideas.

The countdown to take-off had begun: 5, 4, 3...

view of Earth
blinding
MASSIVE
food
FLOATING
BLACK HOLE
air
EXPLOSION
stars
freezing
ROCKET FUEL
discovery

CAFÉ CULTURE

CITY CAFÉ

Looking at this café from above, how many people are here? There are two people under each blue parasol, three under each green one and four under each pink one.

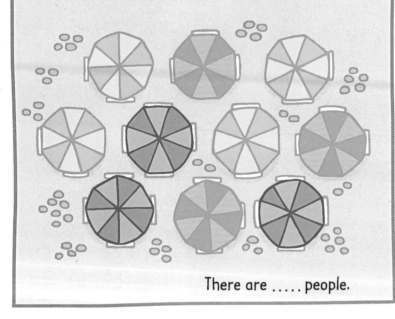

There are ..... people.

OOPS!

A clumsy waiter has dropped a full tray. How many things has he dropped altogether?

He's dropped ..... things.

TASTY BITES

There are many delicious things to eat on this menu, but it doesn't make sense. See if you can figure out what it should say, and write the words correctly.

MENU

PUOS ELBATEGEV	Soup Vegetable
HCIWDNAS IMALAS	....
EKAC ETALOCOHC	....
TRAT YRREBWARTS	....
ECIUJ EGNARO	....
EADNUS MAERC ECI	....
DALAS TIURF	....

EXTRA OLIVE

A customer has ordered a salad without any olives, but someone's accidentally added one green one. Can you spot it?

FANTASTIC FESTIVALS Pages 30-31

ON THE ROAD

Pages 44-45

AFRICAN ADVENTURE
Pages 54–55

WINTER IN SCANDINAVIA
Pages 58–59

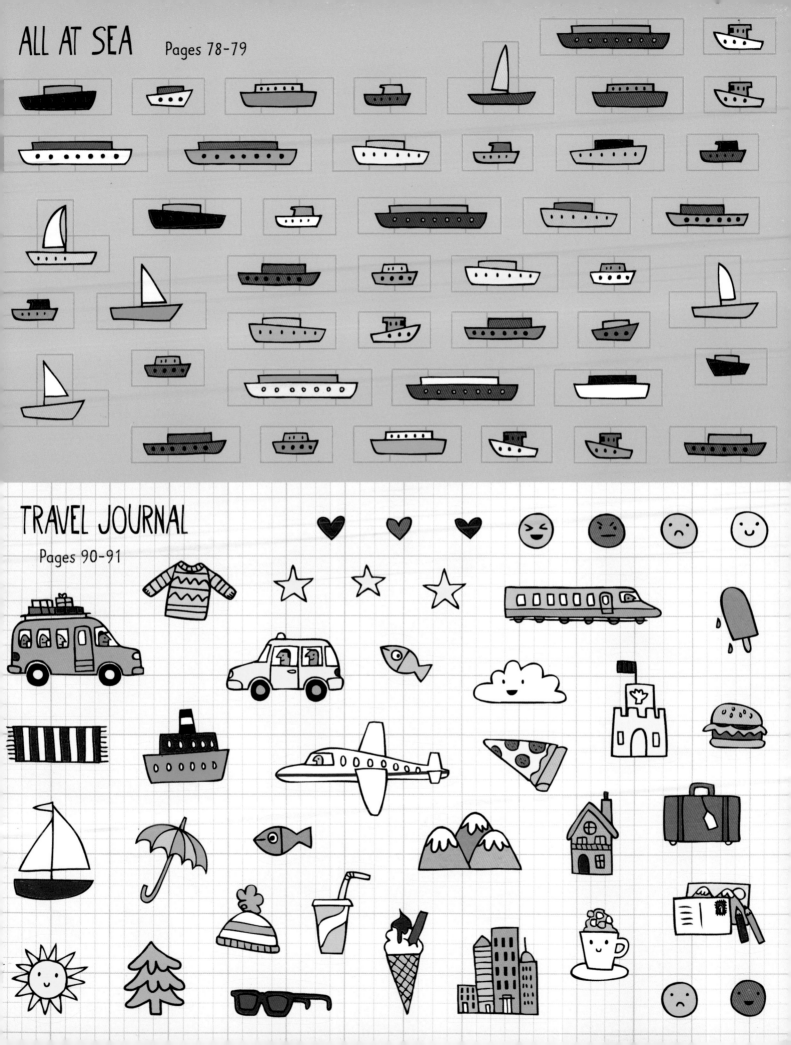

ALL AT SEA

Pages 78-79

TRAVEL JOURNAL

Pages 90-91

ART GALLERY VISIT
LOOKING AROUND

Millie, Billy, Polly and Ollie are at an art gallery. Which item does each of them like best? Draw a line to link each child to the correct work of art.

I love sculptures that don't look like something real.

Millie

I like pictures of people, but I don't like green very much.

Billy

I love animals and prefer drawings to paintings or sculptures.

Polly

I like paintings of places with lots of buildings.

Ollie

BE INSPIRED...

Draw your own travel-related pictures to go in the gallery's collection.

Turn this shape into a boat.

Make this shape into a car.

BUSY INDIA
MARKET DAY

There's lots going on in this bustling scene.
Can you spot all of these in the picture?

QUICK QUIZ

Take this quiz to see how much you know about India.
Draw a line under each correct answer.

1. If someone refers to a 'monsoon', which of these
are they talking about?
A timetable / Heavy seasonal rain / A mythical monster

2. Which of these would you find in India?
The Taj Mahal / The Acropolis / The Statue of Liberty

3. During the festival of Holi, which of these do
people throw at each other?
Tomatoes / Bright powder / Paper airplanes

4. What would you use to buy something in India?
Rupees / Pesos / Kroner

5. One of these animals is regarded as sacred in India.
Which one?
Horse / Frog / Cow

6. What would an Indian lady do with a sari?
Eat it / Wear it / Dance to it

7. Which of these mountain ranges is partly in India?
The Himalayas / The Andes / The Rockies

HIDDEN PLACES

Can you find these Indian place names in
the wordsearch below? They go across, up,
down and some may even go backward.
Cross them off as you find them.

AGRA ✓   GOA ✓   KASHMIR ✓
AMRITSAR   JAIPUR ✓   MUMBAI ✓
DELHI ✓   KERALA ✓

```
N A O D E L H I E B
A H P T N Z R E K B
L E M U M B A I A S
A I Y S D A P O S F
R M A G R X G L N D
E O U C U K A N M Q
K R D I P E R O I A
S A M R I T S A R Y
B L F T A E P I A T
G O A M J C A R G A
```

RICKSHAW RIDE

This rickshaw driver is taking a man to the bus station.
Which way does he need to go?

BUS STATION

51

TRAIN TRAVEL
SUPER-FAST TRAVEL

Japanese bullet trains go incredibly fast. This one's just left the station. Take it to its destination by drawing a line along the track, as quickly as you can, without going off the track.

START

NIGHT TRAIN

Tommy's on a train at night, looking out of the window. Because it's dark, it's hard for him to see what's outside. Can you help by matching the view he can see with the correct daytime view at the bottom?

This is the view from Tommy's window:

Which of these would the view look like in daylight?

① ② ③ ④

FINISH

ON AND OFF

When this train sets off, there are 15 people on board. At the first station, one person gets off and the people waiting at the station get on. At the second station, two people get off and the people waiting get on, and so on. How many people are on the train when it leaves the last station? The first sum has been done to start you off.

1.

$$15 - 1 + 4 = \text{.....}$$

2.

$$\text{.....} - \text{.....} + \text{.....} = \text{.....}$$

3.

$$\text{.....} - \text{.....} + \text{.....} = \text{.....}$$

4.

5.

$$\text{.....} - \text{.....} + \text{.....} = \text{.....}$$

$$\text{.....} - \text{.....} + \text{.....} = \text{.....}$$

There are .... people on the train.

FAMOUS TRAINS

To discover the names of three well-known trains, cross off each first letter, then every other letter. Draw a line to link each train with the correct description.

1. T O Y R P I W E K N I T F E L X M P U R D E H S Z S

....

2. C E A U V R T O C S D T M A K R A

....

3. Y T I G Q V B

....

A. A high-speed train in France.

B. A luxury long-distance train.

C. A train that travels under the sea.

53

AFRICAN ADVENTURE
STICKER SAFARI

A guide is taking a group of tourists on a safari.
Can you complete the scene with stickers from
the sticker pages?

PENGUIN BEACH

Many penguins live in cold places, but these African penguins can be found on a sunny beach. Which two are identical?

HAIR-RAISING HIPPOS

Some tourists are being taken across a lake in a boat, but they need to avoid the dangerous hippos. Which route goes past fewest hippos?

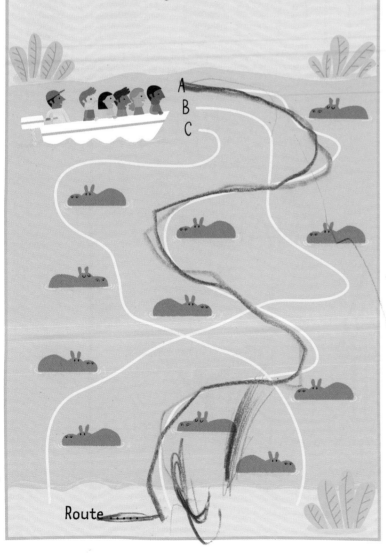

A
B
C

Route . . . . . .

GRAZING GAZELLES

One of these gazelles doesn't have any horns. Can you spot it?

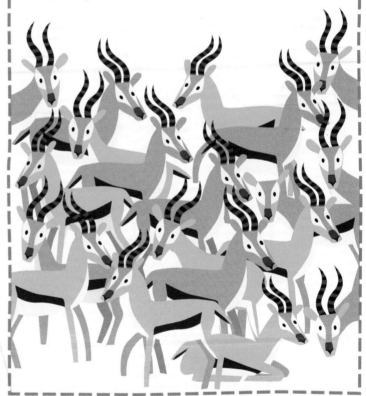

HA HA HA!

Q: Why do lions eat raw meat?

A: Have you ever tried to teach one to cook?

TRAVEL POSTERS

These posters are of travel destinations around the world.
Brighten them up by filling them in with pens or pencils.

SCOTLAND

Amsterdam

THAILAND

Spain

SYDNEY

JAPAN

Morocco

Winter in Scandinavia

The Scandinavian countries are in the far North of Europe, and winter is long and very dark. Complete this wintry scene by pressing on stickers from the sticker pages, filling things in and doodling more pictures.

59

PASSING THE TIME

LOST LETTERS

On a piece of paper, write a message for someone you're with, but leave out some of the letters and draw a line instead.
For example, you could leave out every fourth letter, or all of the vowels (AEIOU). See if they can figure out what it says.

ARE yOU HaVINg A LOnELY _AY? W_ SEE_ TO H_VE B_EN O_ THI_ TRA_N FO_ AGE_, DON'_ WE?

MESSY MUSIC

These headphones are tangled up. Fill in each wire with a different pen, to find out who is listening to each music player.

DRAWING BOXES

Play this with one other person. When you've finished playing it here, you could draw dots on a piece of paper, and play it again.

1. Take turns joining two dots with a vertical or horizontal line.

2. Each time someone completes a box, they write the first letter of their name inside it, then draw another line.

3. The person who completes the most boxes is the winner.

60

A TO Z GAME

This game is a fun way to test your knowledge of place names. They can be towns, continents, countries, cities, deserts, oceans, rivers – all kinds of places.

1. One person starts by naming a place beginning with 'A'. The next person names a place beginning with 'B'.

2. Continue in the same way. If someone can't think of a place, then they can pass. Each person can pass twice and then they're out.

3. If two players or more are still playing by Z, they go back to A and continue until only one person is still playing.

Antarctica

Berlin

...Oslo!

Peru

Q... Q...? Pass!

Z...? Zambia!

Amazon River

(You can also play this game using different themes, such as types of food or animals.)

NEWSPAPER CODE

Write a message for a friend using a newspaper. Draw a dot above each letter you want to use in your message. The letters need to be in the correct order.

DOODLE SHAPES

Draw on these shapes to turn them into things you might see on your travels. You could draw more shapes on another piece of paper, too.

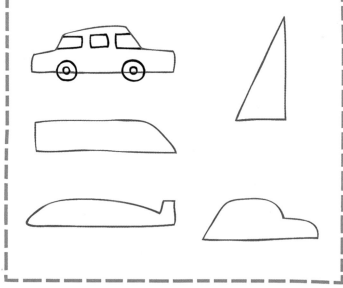

SHARK-INFESTED WAT

In further world travel news, there has been an increase in the number of sharks spotted off the coast of Florida.

A spinner shark

Florida waters are home to a number of shark species, but the recent increase is largely due to spinner sharks migrating North. Spinner sharks like to eat small, bony fish, and will sometimes eat bigger things like stingrays and octopus. They hunt by swimming through schools of fish while spinning around and snapping their mouths, according to experts.

------- What does this message say?

....

....

LOTS TO SEE AND DO

ON THE PIER
There are lots of activities on this pier.

Can you spot two identical toys that you can win at the coconut shy?

The hoopla prizes are all supposed to be toys. Can you spot four things that shouldn't be here?

Roll up... Roll up...

Hoopla

CASTLE VISIT

Christo is taking photos of a ruined castle. He's used the zoom mode on his camera for some, but not for others. Can you find each thing he's photographed in the main picture?

Who has hooked a duck?

Amy   Bill   Claire   Dee

Is the balloon seller holding more red or pink balloons? Draw a line under the correct answer:

Red / Pink

How many people can you see sliding down? ....

COUNTRYSIDE

These two pictures are of the same scene — on a sunny day and in the rain. Apart from the weather, what has changed? There are eight differences — can you spot and draw around them all?

JUMBLED BUILDINGS

Cuba has many beautiful buildings and amazing old classic cars.
Use pens and pencils to brighten up this scene.

ISLANDS IN THE SUN
INVESTIGATING ISLANDS

How much do you know about islands?
Test your knowledge here.

1. In Indonesia, there is a group of islands called the Herb Islands.

True / False

2. Which of these is not an island?

Greenland
Madagascar
Costa Rica

3. Is St. Michael's Mount in Cornwall always an island?

Yes / No

4. Which of these exist?

Kangaroo Island
Giraffe Island
Penguin Island
Canary Islands

5. In the 1960s, a new island emerged from the sea off the coast of Iceland.

True / False

6. Which of these doesn't exist?

Easter Island
Birthday Island
Christmas Island

7. Which of these is furthest South?

The Isles of Scilly
The Seychelles
The Faroe Islands

8. New York City is built on a cluster of islands.

True / False

FISHING FLEET

Arlo, Milo and Jago live on an island and each need to catch a certain number of fish to feed the islanders. Will they catch what they need? Draw an 'X' on each fish as you count it, then draw a line under the correct answer.

YES / NO

Arlo
3 x
4 x
1 x

Milo
5 x
3 x
3 x

Jago
4 x
2 x
3 x

YOUR OWN ISLANDS

Imagine if the islands below were all yours.
Using pens or pencils, design what the islands might look like.

☆ To start with, draw the big things. Here are some ideas:

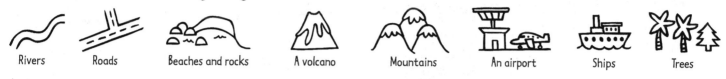

| Rivers | Roads | Beaches and rocks | A volcano | Mountains | An airport | Ships | Trees |

☆ Then, add people, cars, animals, and anything else you'd like to have.

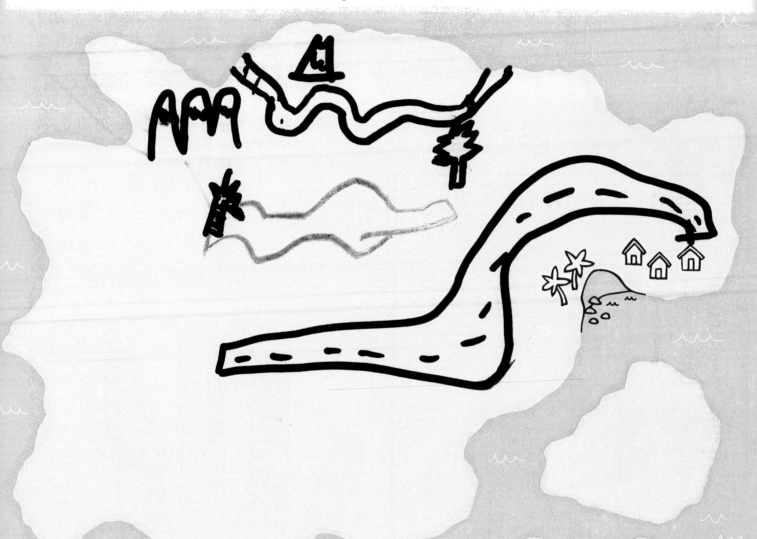

See how many shorter words you can
make from the letters in the word

ARCHIPELAGO

(An archipelago is a group of islands.)

Only use each letter the number
of times it appears in the word.
Try to find at least 15 words.

Space to write
your words

WORLD CRAFTS

Here are just some of the interesting things you might see if you travel to different places.

MEXICAN PIÑATA

At celebrations in Mexico, many people have a piñata – a papier mâché shape filled with treats. People take turns to hit it with a stick until it breaks and everything falls out.
This piñata has just broken open – can you spot one pink treat?

PRETTY PAPERCRAFT

In Poland, people cut paper to make symmetrical decorations, with each half an exact reflection of the other. Draw and fill in the missing half of this decoration.

HENNA HANDS

On special occasions, people in India have patterns painted on their hands with henna, a natural dye. Create a pattern all over this hand.

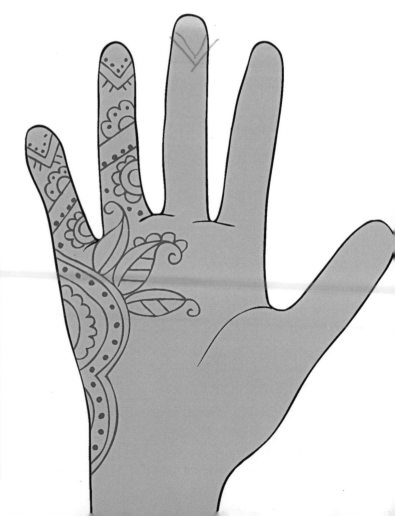

KIRIGAMI CIRCLES

Paper-folding crafts are popular in Japan. In origami, you can only fold the paper. In kirigami, you can cut the paper, too. To make a kirigami circle, you'll need a piece of thin paper, a pair of scissors and a bowl.

1. Draw around the bowl on the piece of paper. Cut out the circle.

2. Fold the paper circle in half, then in half again.

3. Draw half a leaf against each fold. Add little shapes around the circle's edge.

4. Cut out all the shapes. Then, unfold the paper circle.

Here are some other shapes you could try:

 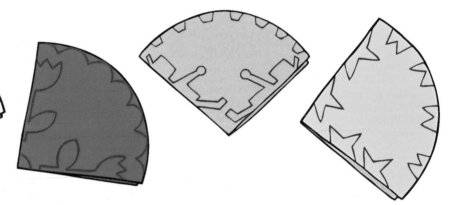

PERFECT PATTERN

You might see tiles similar to these if you visit North Africa or parts of Spain. Fill them in so they are all the same.

MARKET DAY

SHADOW SHAPES

These souvenirs are from around the world. Can you match each souvenir to its shadow shape? Draw a line between the two.

BUSY DAY

The picture on the left shows a stall when it opened in the morning. The picture on the right shows it in the evening. Which six items have been sold during the day? Draw a circle in the space left by each one.

WEIGHING SPICES

These spices from India are being weighed. The first two sets of scales are balanced, but the third set shouldn't be, as one side is actually heavier than the other. Which spice is heavier, yellow or orange?

BROKEN PLATES

These broken plates are decorated with sets of letters. Draw lines between the letters to make complete words.

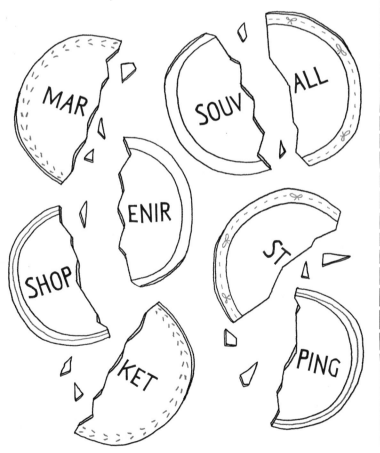

MAR

SOUV

ALL

ENIR

SHOP

ST

KET

PING

FLOWER STALL

This stall is selling fresh flowers and plants. Fill the spaces with lots more.

THE GREAT OUTDOORS

WHERE TO CAMP?

Can you find a place to pitch your tent? In the squares immediately around it (up, down, left, right and diagonally), it must have:

☆ Three trees
☆ One camp fire
☆ No bears

Draw a tent in the correct square.

TREE PATTERN

Draw more tree shapes on the grid, then fill them in with green pens or pencils.

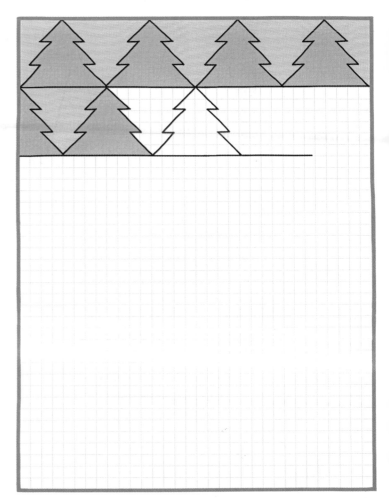

CANOEING Can you find a safe path for this canoe down the river?

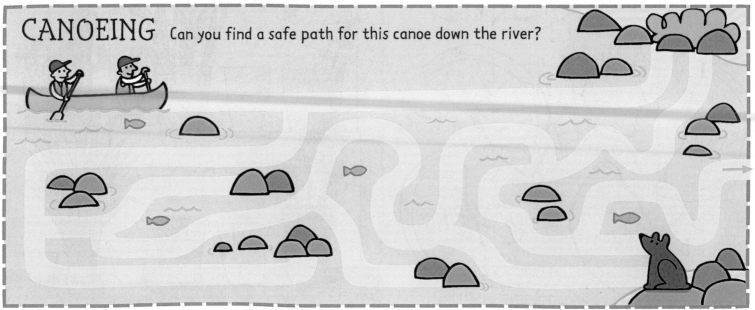

72

BACK TO CAMP

Maria, Juan and Sam are riding back to summer camp. Who gets back first? Add up the numbers on each path – whoever is on the path with the highest total will get back to camp first.

.... gets back to camp first.

CAMPFIRE

Join the dots to light this campfire.

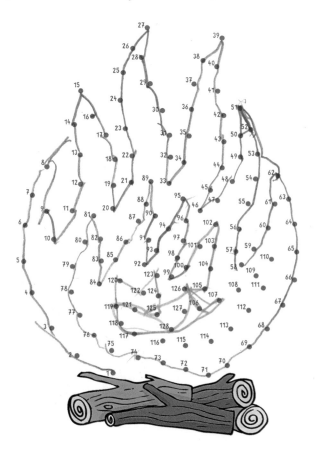

CAMPING GEAR

How many camping objects can you count below?

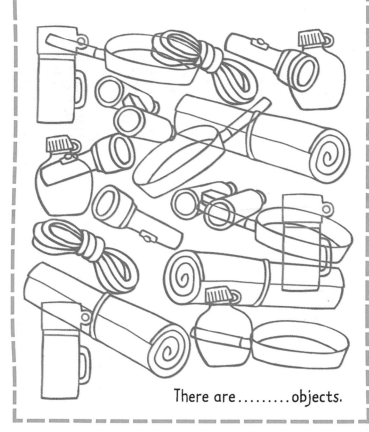

There are .... objects.

73

EXPLORING CHINA
GLOWING LANTERNS

Lantern festivals are celebrated with spectacular displays.
Brighten this display by filling in the lanterns.

GREEDY PANDAS

Giant pandas live in the wild in China.
Draw more pandas amongst the bamboo.

Draw a head and a body.

Add the arms, legs and ears.

Fill in parts of the panda.

A LONG WALL

People travel from all over the world to see the Great Wall of China. In this picture, are there more people taking photos than not taking them?

.... people are taking a photo.

.... people are not taking a photo.

NOODLE TIME

Which of these bowls of noodles is this girl eating from?

A   B   C   D

TERRACOTTA ARMY

Three of the soldiers below are wearing something surprising. Can you spot them?

DESERT ADVENTURE

Dan and Jake are taking part in a car rally in the desert. They need to get to the finish, but lots of routes are blocked by other cars, or cars that have broken down or crashed. Which way do they need to go? They can only <u>overtake</u> moving cars if there's enough room to go past.

PHOTO CALL

These two photos of the race should be identical, but they're not. Can you spot and draw around the five differences between them?

This is Luca. Can you find his car in the main picture?

See if you can spot a vehicle that you wouldn't expect to see in a car race.

How many moving cars did Dan and Jake overtake to get here?

Write the answer here: ....

ALL AT SEA
CRUISE SHIP

Michael is in his cabin. Can you help him get to the swimming pool? He can go up and down stairs and ladders, and go through open doors.

SAIL BOAT

How many triangles can you count on this boat?

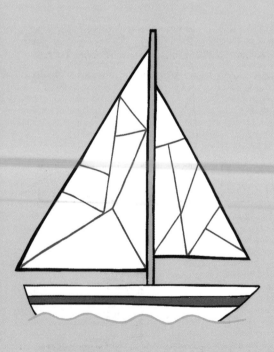

There are .... triangles.

SAILING TRIP

These boats are sailing together, but some have been blown off course. Which boats reach the island? ....

BUSY MARINA

Everyone's coming back from a day at sea. How many boats and ships from the sticker pages can you fit on the water, without any of them overlapping? You may have some extra stickers left over.

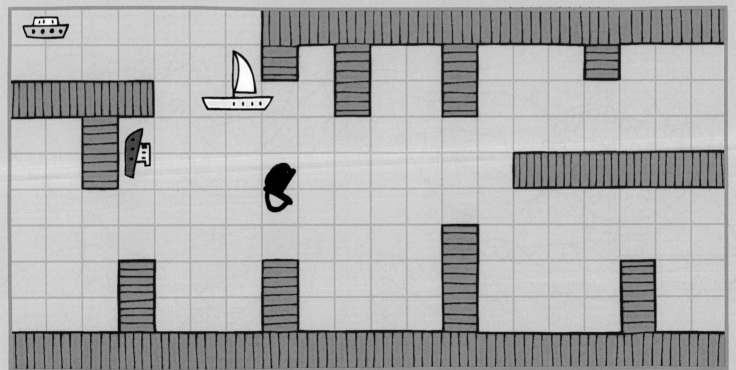

A FLOATING CITY

The Italian city of Venice is built on a group of islands. From a distance, it appears to float on the sea.

GONDOLA RACE

Three gondoliers are racing along the canals to collect people from a hotel. Who wins? Follow each route, counting the points as you go. The one with the lowest score gets there first.

POINTS — Low bridge = 4 — Boat to pass = 3 — Choppy water = 2 — Clear water = -1

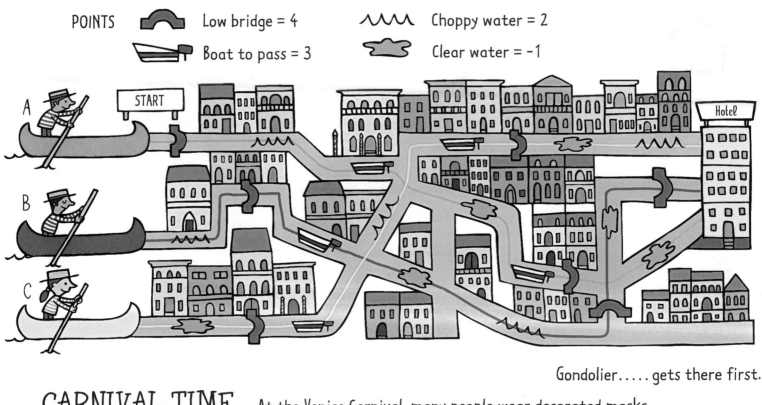

Gondolier..... gets there first.

CARNIVAL TIME

At the Venice Carnival, many people wear decorated masks.

Doodle decorations on these masks.

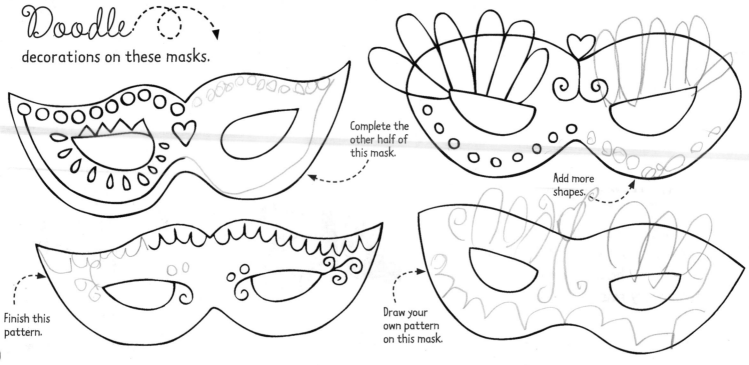

Complete the other half of this mask.

Add more shapes.

Finish this pattern.

Draw your own pattern on this mask.

IN THE SQUARE

Lots of people are enjoying a sunny day in St. Mark's Square. Can you spot the following?

- ☆ A man with a child on his shoulders
- ☆ A girl with a teddy bear
- ☆ Three street lamps
- ☆ A boy with a balloon
- ☆ Someone eating an ice cream
- ☆ Three dogs
- ☆ Ten pigeons
- ☆ A waitress serving drinks

DID YOU KNOW?

Venice floods when the tides and wind produce an 'acqua alta' (high water). People have to walk around on temporary raised walkways.

Under the sea

If you go snorkelling or scuba diving, you may see an amazing underwater world. To complete this picture, fill in each numbered shape with the correct pen or pencil.

1 – orange
2 – yellow
3 – blue
4 – red
5 – light green
6 – dark green
7 – purple

GREAT EXPLORERS

LOST SHIP

In the 1830s, English scientist Charles Darwin sailed to the Galapagos Islands in search of exotic new animal species. Which square is his ship in, on this map?

The ship is: ☆ East of a volcano ☆ South of a seal colony
☆ In a square with no land in it

KEY:
Seal colony
Volcano
Tortoise nest
Dolphin pod

FIND A NEW SPECIES

One of these Galapagos animals is a new species and doesn't appear in the identification book. Pair up the animals with the ones in the book, to find out which is the new species.

DID YOU KNOW?

The reason Native Americans are sometimes called 'Indians' is due to the Italian explorer, Christopher Columbus.

In 1492, he sailed across the Atlantic Ocean to America. Thinking he had reached India, he called the first people he met 'Indians'.

ICY ADVENTURE

In 1911, Norwegian Roald Amundsen was the first explorer to reach the South Pole. Which route should he take to get back to his camp?

....

A
B
C
D

JUNGLE JOURNEY

Around 1800, German scientist Alexander von Humboldt trekked through the Amazon rainforest and discovered native tribes. Which route should he take to go past as many people as possible? He can't go along any route twice.

He passes .... people.

FINISH

UP IN THE AIR

TAKE YOUR SEATS

This family is on a plane, waiting to take off. Doodle their faces and complete their clothes, then fill in the picture.

WHERE TO?

These planes are all flying to different places. To find out where each one is going, follow its trail and write the letters underneath.

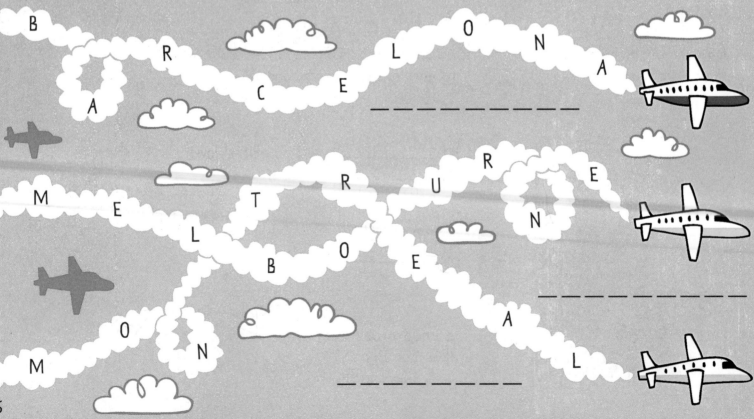

PLACE TO PLACE

Stan and Dan travel a lot by plane. Stan only flies along blue routes and Dan only flies along red ones. Who visits more places on their way back to Frankfurt airport? Follow the arrows from airport to airport to find out – airports with no onward route don't count.

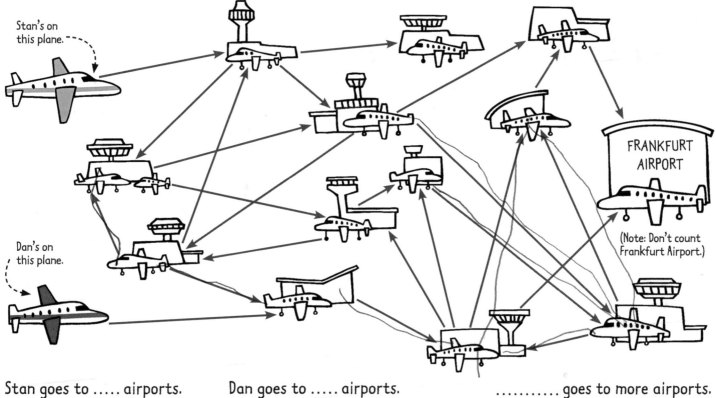

Stan's on this plane.

Dan's on this plane.

FRANKFURT AIRPORT

(Note: Don't count Frankfurt Airport.)

Stan goes to ..... airports.   Dan goes to ..... airports.   .... goes to more airports.

TRUE OR FALSE?

A jumbo jet can weigh as much as 100 elephants.

FLYING HIGH

Here are three landmarks as seen from the air.
Link each one to its name and place with a line.

A

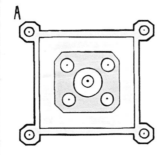

1. The Eiffel Tower, Paris, France

B

C

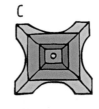

2. The Statue of Liberty, New York City, USA

3. The Taj Mahal, Agra, India

CATCHING A WAVE

SURFBOARD SUDOKU

Draw pictures of these four patterned surfboards on this grid. Every row, column and 4-square box must have one picture of each surfboard in it.

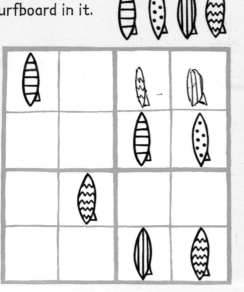

SURFERS

Can you spot five differences between these surfers? Draw a circle around each one.

MISSING PIECE

Which of the squares isn't in the picture?

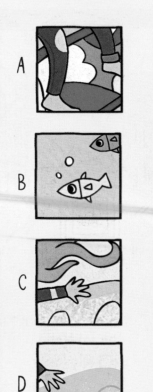

A

B

C

D

QUICK QUIZ

Can you answer these surfing questions?

1. What is it called when a surfer puts one foot at the front of their board and wraps their toes over the edge?

a) hanging five   b) hanging ten   c)monkey foot

2. What does 'surf's up' mean?

a) my surfboard is upside down   b) the waves look good for surfing   c) the tide is in

3. What are 'foamies'?

a) small bubbling waves   b) types of wetsuits   c) soft surfboards often used by beginners

4. What is a wipeout?

a) winning a surfing competition   b) falling off your surfboard   c) cleaning your surfboard

MAKING WAVES   Doodle more surfers riding the waves.

Continue the wave pattern to the bottom of the page, then fill it in.

TRAVEL JOURNAL

Whether you're out and about, away on a trip or at home dreaming of adventures you'd like to have, you can fill these pages with experiences, memories, thoughts, ideas, doodles, and stickers from the sticker pages...

IDEAS

☆ What did you see?

☆ What day was it?

☆ Who was with you?

☆ Was the sun shining?

☆ How long did it take?

☆ What did you eat?

☆ What were you wearing?

☆ How did you get there?

☆ How did you feel?

☆ Was it hot or cold?

exciting

SURPRISED

HAPPY

lake

tastes

IMMENSE

Beautiful

ICY

craggy

BUILDINGS

sights

emerald green

SHIPS

quaint

bright

DRAMATIC

busy

choppy

animals

Rose pink

Calm

sounds

stormy

smells

gold

bumpy

ancient

amusing

sky blue

TREES

delicious

fascinating

PRECIPICE

TRAVEL NOTEBOOK

If you go away, you could keep a travel journal in a notebook. Write down what you see and do each day. Where did you go? What did you see? You could glue in souvenirs from your trip: tickets, photos, postcards, maps, stamps... You could also draw pictures of the things you see.

Answers and solutions

2-3 GETTING READY

EARLY START: 6.55

MIX-UP:

WHERE TO GO?: Egypt

PACKING: Yes. She hasn't packed a magazine.

4-5 BUSY AIRPORT

- ○ People reading books
- ○ Someone putting on their shoes
- ○ Men who are asleep
- ○ People pulling suitcases on wheels
- ○ A child playing with a toy car
- ○ Someone eating a sandwich
- ○ A boy riding on a luggage trolley
- ○ Someone buying a magazine
- ○ A lady in an orange top

6-7 GOING PLACES

CITY WALK:
No, they don't walk
past the church.
- ○ Ice cream sign

CROSSING RIVERS:
A = Pedestrian bridge
B = Suspension bridge
C = Rope bridge
D = Ferry
E = Stepping stones

8-9 A WORLD OF FOOD

DIFFERENT TASTES:
Australia = kangaroo steak, Canada = maple syrup, China = chicken feet, England = jellied eels, France = snails in garlic butter, Ghana = goat stew, Italy = folded pizza (calzone), Russia = fish eggs (caviar)

FRUIT AND VEGETABLES:

carrots: C7, J9
avocado: B2
strawberries: I7
lemon: B9
passion fruit: C4
star fruit: I1, J6
tomatoes: C2, A7, B7
butternut squash: J4
Yes, he finds everything.

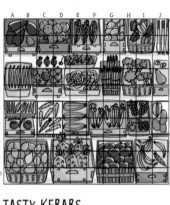

FOOD FINDER:

TASTY KEBABS:

SHARING SUSHI:
No, there isn't.

10-11 WHEN IN ROME

IN THE FORUM:

MOPED MAZE:

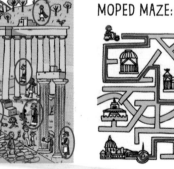

GELATO JOY:

Milo wants STRAWBERRY   Sophia wants CHOCOLATE
Teresa wants VANILLA   Nico wants PISTACHIO

16-17 A VISIT TO RUSSIA

TRANS-SIBERIAN RAILWAY: C   **RUSSIAN DOLLS:** D

QUICK QUIZ:
1. Little pancakes 2. True. In mid-summer, Northern Russia has daylight 24 hours a day. 3. Ballet

18-19 PALM TREES AND PYRAMIDS

PILES OF STONE:
1 = mummy, 2 = sand,
3 = desert

THIRSTY CAMELS:
2, 4, 5 and 7 find the oasis.
1, 3 and 6 get lost.

MUSEUM TREASURES:

SECRETS OF THE SPHINX:
1. lion   2. Giza   3. True   4. East   5. a headdress

20-21 STUNNING SOUTH AMERICA

LUSH RAINFOREST: Puffin

HERDING ON HORSEBACK:

Light brown. There are
nine light brown cows,
eight dark brown cows
and two white cows.

ANCIENT STONES: 3

FUN FABRICS:
A = ☐ B = ☐ C = ☐

22-23 EXCITING SPORTS

HANG-GLIDING: C, B, D, A

RIDING THE RAPIDS:
He takes route B.

- ○ deer
- ○ wolf
- ○ birds
- ○ bear
- ○ rabbits

26-27 IN THE CITY

BIRDS ON WINDOW LEDGES: 18

MAZE:

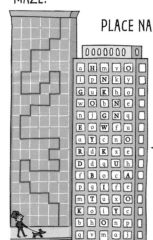

PLACE NAMES:

Hong Kong,
New York,
Dubai,
Tokyo

WINDOWS:

- B
- C
- D
- A

SUDOKU PUZZLES:

Top   Middle   Bottom

28-29 TRAIN TRIP

Sadie

30-31 FANTASTIC FESTIVALS

CARNIVAL COSTUMES: D

34-35 AT THE SEASIDE

A DAY ON THE BEACH:
No. There are five people
and only four balls.

IN... AND OUT...

ON THE SEA FRONT:

Asha

Ruby

CHOPPY SEA:

SEAL SANCTUARY: Seal 11

36-37 BIG WORLD QUIZ

1. a	2. b	3. a	4. b
5. c	6. c	7. c	8. b
9. a	10. a	11. b	12. a
13. c	14. b	15. b	16. a
17. b	18. c	19. c	20. b
21. c	22. a	23. c	24. b
25. c	26. b	27. a	28. a
29. a	30. c	31. a	32. c
33. a	34. c	35. c	36. b

38-39 AWESOME AUSTRALIA

GOING WALKABOUT: D = stream, B = starting point

SIGHTSEEING CONUNDRUM:

A = 19 smiles,
B = 20 smiles,
C = 21 smiles.
Dom will visit
C – The Great
Barrier Reef.

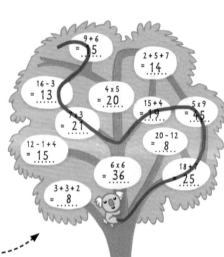

SLEEPY KOALA:

40-41 HIKING AND BIKING

HAPPY HIKER:

TRIPLET HIKERS:

STRANGE THINGS:

BRAVE BIKERS:

Biker C won, with 14 points.
A and B each have 15 points.

○ abandoned bike
○ lost hiker

42-43 ON TOP OF THE WORLD

WHICH MOUNTAIN?:

1 = Mount Kilimanjaro,
2 = Uluru, 3 = Mount
Fuji, 4 = Devils Tower

WILD FLOWERS: 28

PRAYER FLAGS:

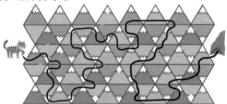

CLIMBING HIGH:

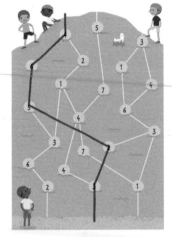

MOUNTAIN CROSSING:

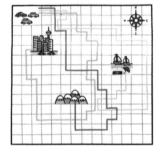

44-45 ON THE ROAD

WHO GOES WHERE?:

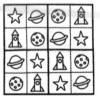

WHICH ORDER?:

Blue, green, red, white

THINGS TO SEE:

Tilly: 'dow' (cow) = 4, 'iouse'
(house) = 4. Tom: 'woc' (cow)
= 5, 'esuoh' (house) = 3. Tom
has seen more cows, Tilly has
seen more houses.

46-47 SPACE TRAVEL

READY TO GO?:
A has no boots
B has no camera
C has no spacesuit

SPACE SUDOKU:

BLAST OFF!:
planet
gravity
meteor
galaxy
sun

SPACE DESTINATIONS:

1 = MOON, 2 = MARS,
3 = JUPITER, 4 =
SATURN, 5 = URANUS

48 CAFÉ CULTURE

CITY CAFÉ: 29 people

OOPS!: 26 things

EXTRA OLIVE:

TASTY BITES:

PUOS ELBATEGEV = vegetable soup,
HCIWDNAS IMALAS = salami sandwich,
EKAC ETALOCOHC = chocolate cake, TRAT YRREBWARTS =
strawberry tart, ECIUJ EGNARO = orange juice, EADNUS
MAERC ECI = ice cream sundae, DALAS TIURF = fruit salad

49 ART GALLERY VISIT

LOOKING
AROUND:

  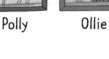

Millie   Billy   Polly   Ollie

50-51 BUSY INDIA

MARKET DAY:

RICKSHAW RIDE:

HIDDEN PLACES:

```
N A O O D E L H I E B
A H P T N Z R E K S D
L E M U M B A I A H E
A I Y S D A P O S A L
R M A G R X G L H M I
E O U C U K A N I Q A
K R D I P E R O R A Y
S A M R I T S A R R O
B L F T A E P I A T
G O A M U C A R G A
```

QUICK QUIZ:

1 = Heavy seasonal rain
2 = The Taj Mahal
3 = Bright powder
4 = Rupees
5 = Cow
6 = Wear it
7 = The Himalayas

52-53 TRAIN TRAVEL

NIGHT TRAIN: 4

ON AND OFF:
10 people. Station 1. 15 - 1 + 4 = 18, Station 2.
18 - 2 + 3 = 19, Station 3. 19 - 3 + 0 = 16,
Station 4. 16 - 4 + 2 = 14, Station 5. 14 - 5 + 1 = 10.

FAMOUS TRAINS:
1 = B = Orient Express, 2 = C = Eurostar, 3 = A = TGV

54-55 AFRICAN ADVENTURE

PENGUIN BEACH:

HAIR-RAISING HIPPOS: B

GRAZING GAZELLES:

60-61 PASSING THE TIME

LOST LETTERS:
ARE YOU HAVING A LOVELY DAY? WE SEEM TO HAVE BEEN
ON THIS TRAIN FOR AGES, DON'T WE?

MESSY MUSIC:
Girl = black music player
Boy = white music player

NEWSPAPER CODE:
I would like to see
a shark some time.

62-63 LOTS TO SEE AND DO

COCONUT SHY: HOOPLA:

DUCKS: Claire   BALLOONS: Pink   SLIDE: 9

CASTLE VISIT: COUNTRYSIDE:

66-67 ISLANDS IN THE SUN

INVESTIGATING ISLANDS:
1 = False, 2 = Costa Rica, 3 = No, 4 = All of them exist,
apart from Giraffe Island, 5 = True, Surtsey appeared,
6 = Birthday Island, 7 = The Seychelles, 8 = True

FISHING FLEET: No

68-69 WORLD CRAFTS

MEXICAN PIÑATA:

70-71 MARKET DAY

SHADOW
SHAPES:

BUSY DAY:

WEIGHING SPICES: Yellow
BROKEN PLATES:
MAR-KET, SHOP-PING,
SOUV-ENIR, ST-ALL

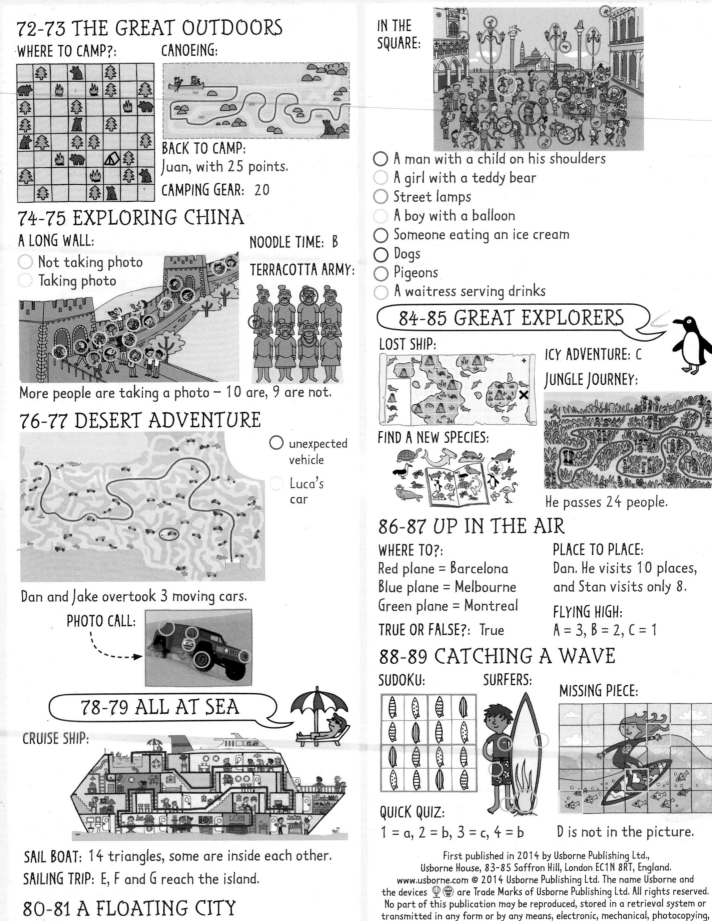

72-73 THE GREAT OUTDOORS

WHERE TO CAMP?:

CANOEING:

BACK TO CAMP: Juan, with 25 points.

CAMPING GEAR: 20

74-75 EXPLORING CHINA

A LONG WALL:
- ○ Not taking photo
- ○ Taking photo

NOODLE TIME: B

TERRACOTTA ARMY:

More people are taking a photo – 10 are, 9 are not.

76-77 DESERT ADVENTURE

- ○ unexpected vehicle
- ○ Luca's car

Dan and Jake overtook 3 moving cars.

PHOTO CALL:

78-79 ALL AT SEA

CRUISE SHIP:

SAIL BOAT: 14 triangles, some are inside each other.

SAILING TRIP: E, F and G reach the island.

80-81 A FLOATING CITY

GONDOLA RACE: A gets there first, with 14 points.

IN THE SQUARE:
- ○ A man with a child on his shoulders
- ○ A girl with a teddy bear
- ○ Street lamps
- ○ A boy with a balloon
- ○ Someone eating an ice cream
- ○ Dogs
- ○ Pigeons
- ○ A waitress serving drinks

84-85 GREAT EXPLORERS

LOST SHIP:

ICY ADVENTURE: C

JUNGLE JOURNEY:

FIND A NEW SPECIES:

He passes 24 people.

86-87 UP IN THE AIR

WHERE TO?:
Red plane = Barcelona
Blue plane = Melbourne
Green plane = Montreal

TRUE OR FALSE?: True

PLACE TO PLACE:
Dan. He visits 10 places, and Stan visits only 8.

FLYING HIGH:
A = 3, B = 2, C = 1

88-89 CATCHING A WAVE

SUDOKU:

SURFERS:

MISSING PIECE:

QUICK QUIZ:
1 = a, 2 = b, 3 = c, 4 = b

D is not in the picture.

First published in 2014 by Usborne Publishing Ltd., Usborne House, 83-85 Saffron Hill, London EC1N 8RT, England. www.usborne.com © 2014 Usborne Publishing Ltd. The name Usborne and the devices ♛ ⊕ are Trade Marks of Usborne Publishing Ltd. All rights reserved.
UE. First Published in America 2014.